Sticker Shapes
CHRISTMAS

Designed by
Carly Davies

Words by Sam Smith

You can make all the festive things in this book
using one or more of the stickers at the back.
Then draw on details with a felt-tip pen.

Here's one way you could make a stocking.

Add decorations to the tree, and put some more presents beneath it.

Create your own patterns on
this present's wrapping paper.

Build some more snowmen, and add
hats, faces, and twigs for the arms.

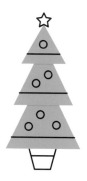

Fill this snowy mountain scene with bright buildings and Christmas trees.

Stick more owls
and birds in the
holly branches.

10

Fill the forest with
a herd of reindeer.

Hang up lots of bright stockings, and give each one a different design.

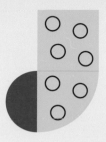

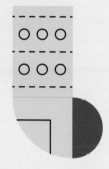

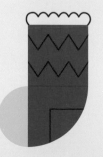

Add the finishing touches to these gingerbread men.

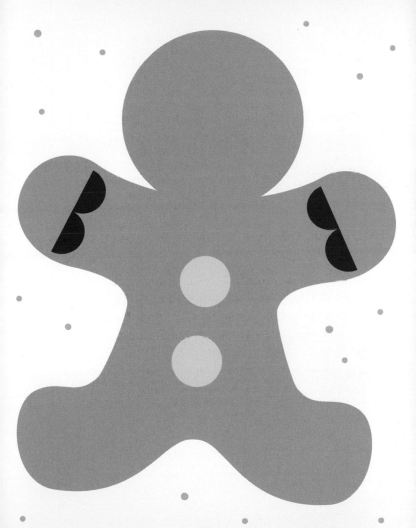

Decorate the page
with festive flowers
and sprigs of holly.

Show lots more penguins in the snow.

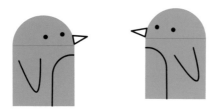

Combine different stickers
to create all kinds of
Christmas decorations.

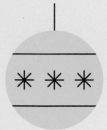

21

Fill the sky with snowflakes
of different shapes and sizes.

Add more leaves and berries to this Christmas wreath.